MORE THAN a REPORT

Nine Social Studies Writing Projects

More Than a Report - a *unique* way to insure *successful, individual* report writing.

Unique - The polished look of the finished product, complete with a three-dimensional visual, makes these projects "more than a report."

Successful - The simple, structured format allows each student to complete reports regardless of skill level.

Individual - Students work on their own topics within the same theme. Students can work cooperatively while producing their own report.

More Than a Report - appeals to all learning styles.

MORE THAN a REPORT

Materials List

Here are the materials you will need for the reports in this book. Materials for each report are also listed on the Teacher Information Page for every report.

Most of the materials are everyday school supplies; a few will need to be purchased.

Needed for all reports:

- file folder or 12" x 18" (30.5 x 46 cm) construction paper folder per student

- copy paper— at least four pages per student

- glue to attach reproducibles to the inside of the folder. Rubber cement gives the nicest results, but is NOT to be used by students. An adult will need to assemble the completed folders if rubber cement is used.

- markers, crayons, or colored pencils

Needed for some reports:

- chenille stems (pipe cleaners)

- cardboard— plain, brown, sturdy cardboard that boxes are made from. Tagboard is not stiff enough.

- index cards— for note-taking

- bamboo skewers or straws

- modeling clay

- foil stars

- school milk cartons

- scrap construction paper

- white glue

How to Make More Than a Report a Snap!

Research Skills

The ability and experience level of your class will determine how much teaching or reviewing of research skills is needed. Obviously, these reports will be more successful if your class has had practice with research strategies, note-taking skills, and bibliography entries.

How to Assign the Reports

All reports will be individualized. Many use the annotated list at the end of the directions. You can assign the report in several ways:

- let students choose their topic
- you assign each topic
- let them pick a topic out of a hat
- assign reports alphabetically

Student Direction Sheets

All reports come with two "Student Direction Sheets." These will help you assign the report and guide your students along the way. Discuss every step of the directions with your students, modeling where appropriate. Assess understanding of each section before going on. Explain that the box in front of each step is for them to check off each completed step. The first time you do a report, keep samples or take pictures of finished products to use with future classes.

Hint: make overlays of the reproducible forms for each report. Display them on the screen as you go over the directions, pointing out each section as it is explained.

Lined-Paper Masters

The final copy of most of the reports is completed on unlined paper. To help students write neatly and in a straight line, make up a class set of lined masters:

- take one sheet of ruled paper (the kind they use every day)
- trace over each line using a ruler and a fine-tipped black marker
- photocopy a class set
- laminate

Students paper clip blank paper to the master; the guidelines show through.

Bibliography Formats

A number of **More Than a Report** projects require students to list resources used in a bibliography.

On the inside back cover, you will find a chart showing how to write bibliographic entries for several types of resources. Reproduce for each student or post for student reference.

Pipe-Cleaner People

Four reports (**All About Me**, **Women of America**, **Black Americans**, and **Incredible People**) use pipe-cleaner people as an engaging visual. These are easy to make and pose. They can be dressed in a variety of materials and still be light enough to attach to a piece of cardboard for display.

Practice making a pipe cleaner person yourself before guiding students through the process. Give directions one step at a time; don't go on to the next step until **everyone** is ready.

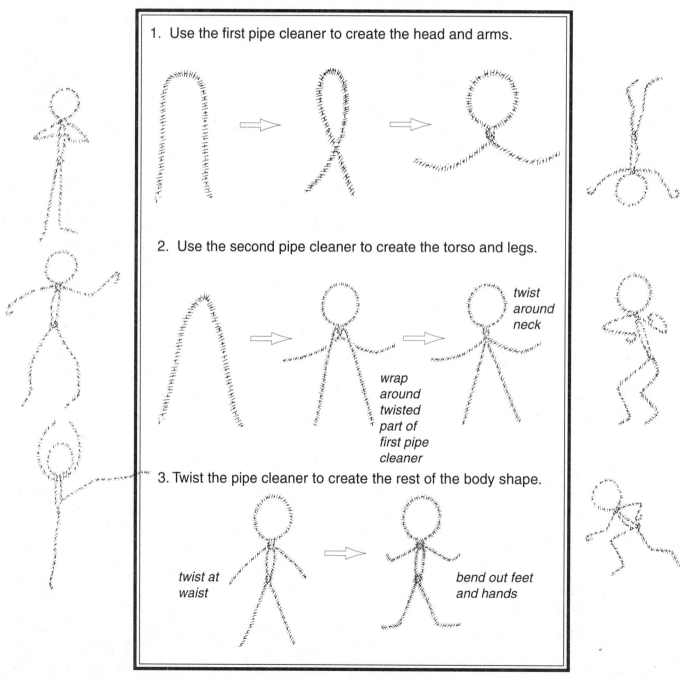

1. Use the first pipe cleaner to create the head and arms.

2. Use the second pipe cleaner to create the torso and legs.

twist around neck

wrap around twisted part of first pipe cleaner

3. Twist the pipe cleaner to create the rest of the body shape.

twist at waist

bend out feet and hands

Your pipe cleaner person can be posed in any position, performing any feat—dancing, sitting, jumping, even standing on its head! Caution children not to bend the "people" too many times— they start to look "strange."

Pipe-cleaner people can be dressed in construction paper, fabric, aluminum foil, doll clothes, or a combination of materials. The people can be dressed in class or sent home to be completed. It's a good family project.

Depending on the age and ability of your group, you may want to make several finished samples yourself to provide completion ideas.

moss, string, yarn hair

faces painted, drawn with pencil, markers, puffy paint

faces made from cotton, paper, felt, or cloth strips glued

clothes made from felt, cloth, paper

make glasses from wire

accessories made from paper, found objects

moveable eyes can be glued on

sand, gravel, etc., glued on cardboard

All About Me

What better way to begin the school year! This report gives all students a chance to express themselves and to let others know how special they are. The finished projects generate classroom conversations about individual uniqueness. They also help to produce a class "team" of individuals who know and understand each other and are thus better able to work together.

Completed reports can be shown off in the library or other areas of the school that get a lot of foot traffic. Each **More Than a Report** is an expression of individuality and creativity. Students contribute their own personal touches. They are very exciting to see!
The completed report is also an excellent memory of their year in your class. It is something that will go in the box of "keepers" that come home from school.
Have fun!

Another excellent time to do this project is just prior to Open House in the spring.

Complete teacher directions for "All About Me" are on page 13.

All About ME

 More Than a Report EMC 558

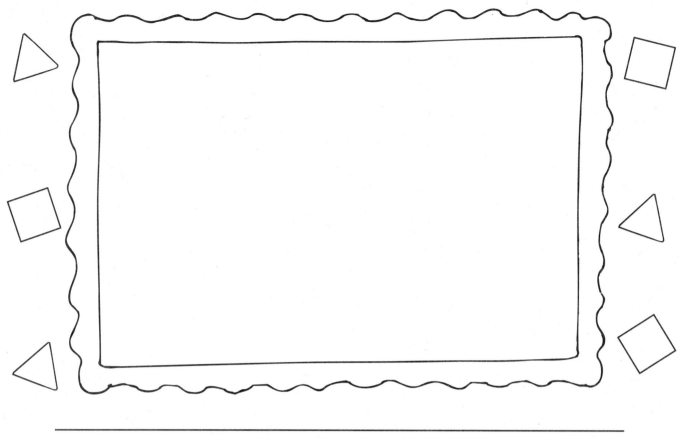

_____

_____

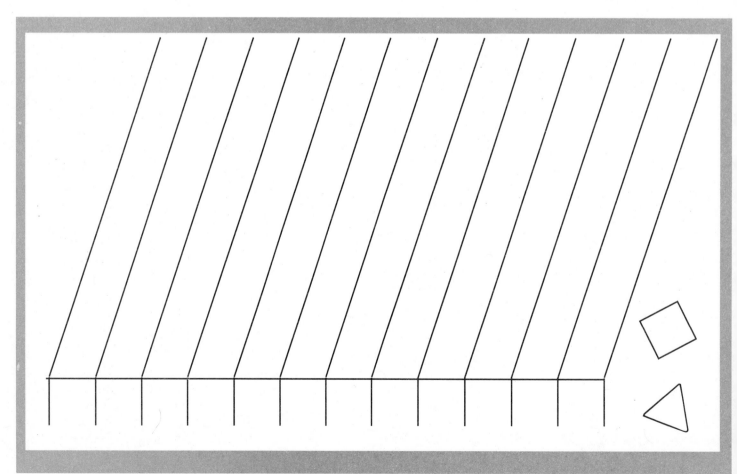

     More Than a Report EMC 558

When I'm an adult...

Someday I will...

My wish for the world...

I'm happiest when...

I would do anything for...

Doing what I do best...

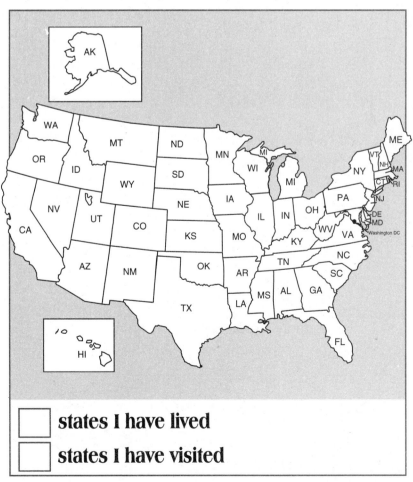

☐ **states I have lived**

☐ **states I have visited**

Name:_____

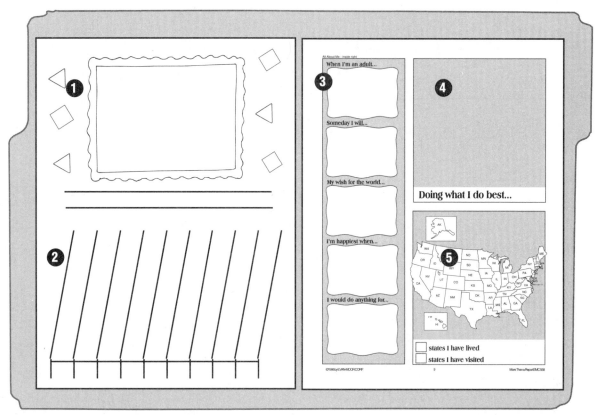

Instructions—The diagram above shows the different parts of your report. Each number in the directions listed on page 11 matches the number above. This is to show you where information is to be placed on your report. Keep these sheets in your folder so you can look at them often. You're going to do an ***awesome*** job and be very proud of your report when you are finished!

☐ Front Cover

Your front cover is not pictured here. To complete the front cover follow these directions:

- Place one letter of your first name in each box.
- On the line after the box write words describing yourself that begin with that letter.
- Separate the words with commas.
- Capitalize them all.
- If your name has fewer letters than the lines given, you can decorate the lines or write more words that describe you. Use your imagination.

Example:

J	Joyful, Just, Japanese
A	Adorable, Amazing
N	Nice, Noisy, Neat, Noble

Name:_____

☐ ❶ Family Picture

• On the paper your teacher gave you, draw a picture of yourself and the people and pets who live with you. This will be glued in *space 1* later.

- Draw just their shoulders and heads.

- Begin in the middle of the paper with yourself.

- Next draw some of the people in the front row on either side of yourself.

- Then draw a back row of people who are taller.

- Fill in the back of the picture so it looks like a wall in your house.

• On the line under the picture, write the names of everyone.

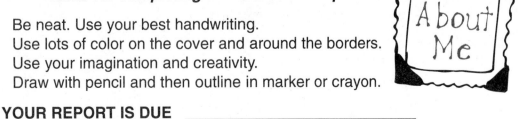

☐ ❷ Time Line
Copy the events from your homework sheet.

☐ ❸ Sentence Completion
Complete the sentences in each bubble. This is a chance to let people know the things that are on your mind. Give each bubble a lot of thought before you finish the sentence.

☐ ❹ Pipe-Cleaner Person
Your piece of cardboard and two pipe cleaners will be used to make YOU.
Your teacher will give directions for making the figure. It is your job to dress the figure and pose it on the cardboard so it represents you *"doing what you do best."* Attach the figure to the cardboard; it will sit in this space on your finished report.

☐ ❺ Map Completion
Copy information from your homework sheet.

Hints for completing an "awesome" report:

Be neat. Use your best handwriting.
Use lots of color on the cover and around the borders.
Use your imagination and creativity.
Draw with pencil and then outline in marker or crayon.

YOUR REPORT IS DUE _____

ALL About Me

Name_____ Date_____

All About Me Report

You will be doing a report called **All About Me**. To prepare, the following two items need to be completed at home with your parent's help.

Map Completion:

Fill in each box of the legend with a different color. Using the two colors you choose, fill in the map, coloring the states where you have lived with one color and the states that you have visited with the other color.

Time line Completion:

Label the first line on the left with the year you were born. Each line represents one more year.

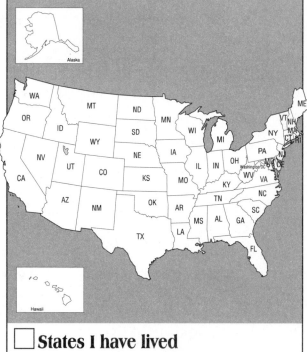

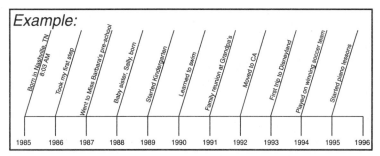

Example:

Born in Nashville, TN 8:03 AM · Took my first step · Went to Miss Barbara's pre-school · Baby sister, Sally, born · Started Kindergarten · Learned to swim · Family reunion at Grandpa's · Moved to CA · First trip to Disneyland · Played on winning soccer team · Started piano lessons

1985 1986 1987 1988 1989 1990 1991 1992 1993 1994 1995 1996

☐ **States I have lived**
☐ **States I have visited**

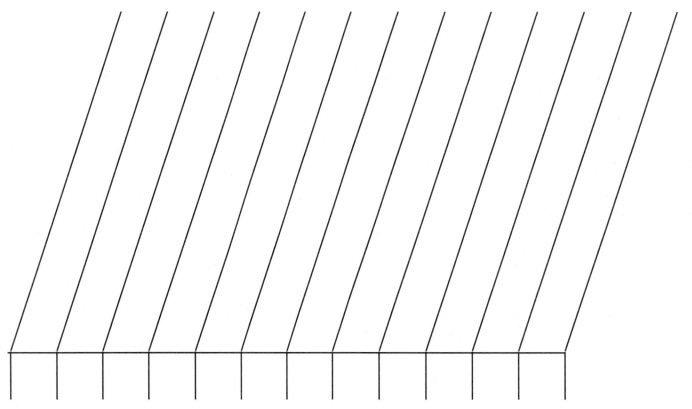

TEACHER DIRECTIONS

Before assigning the report:

1. Prepare materials needed for each student:
   - 1- file folder or folded 12" x 18" (30.5 x 46 cm) construction paper
   - 1- 4" x 4" (10 x 10 cm) piece of cardboard
   - 2 pipe cleaners
   - report reproducibles, pages 7, 8, 9
   - homework sheet, page 12
   - student direction sheets, page 10, 11(fill in date due before photocopying)
   - 1 - 6" x 4" (15 x 10 cm) piece of white drawing paper

2. Assign the homework reproducible. Check each student's homework for completeness before assigning the report.

Assigning the report:

1. Pass out to students:
   - folder and report reproducibles
   - cardboard
   - pipe cleaners
   - student direction sheets
   - white drawing paper
   - completed homework sheet

2. Introduce the report:
   Explain that they will be doing a report on themselves. Have students follow along on their instruction sheet as you explain each section of the report. (see directions, page 3). *Note:* younger groups may need help thinking of descriptive adjectives to use on the front cover. You may wish to brainstorm and post lists of words for their reference.

3. Guide students step by step to make the pipe cleaner person (see directions, pages 4-5).

Working on the report:

- Most of the report can be completed in class.
- The time line and state information from the homework sheet will be transferred.
- Provide resources for pipe cleaner people for students who may need assistance.

Finishing the report:

- Glue the report cover to the outside of the folder.
- Glue reproducibles inside the folder; one on each side.
- Glue completed family picture in appropriate space.

Explorers

Six thousand years ago people knew very little of what existed beyond a few days' journey from their homes. As civilization developed, so did the idea of trading with other countries. This was the beginning of exploration. From the Phoenicians to the Egyptians to the Romans, we can see ever increasing journeys. The Vikings, from the 8th to 12th centuries, were the first to cross the Atlantic Ocean. Whether to set foot on untouched land, or to discover a plant or animal no one has ever seen, humans are fascinated by the idea of "going where no one has gone before."

The goal of this **More Than a Report** is to show the variety of explorers and areas explored. Encourage your students to expand their view of explorers beyond those who journeyed during the "Age of Exploration" during the 15th and 16th centuries. Challenge them to widen their vision of the world, and believe that they too can explore on this seemingly small planet.

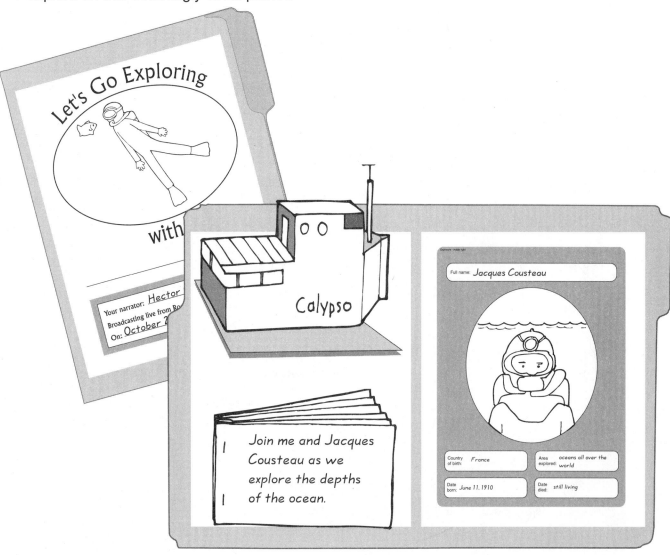

Complete teacher directions for "Explorers" are on page 20.

Let's Go Exploring

with

Your narrator: _____

Broadcasting live from Room: _____

On: _____

Bibliography

_____

_____

_____

_____

_____

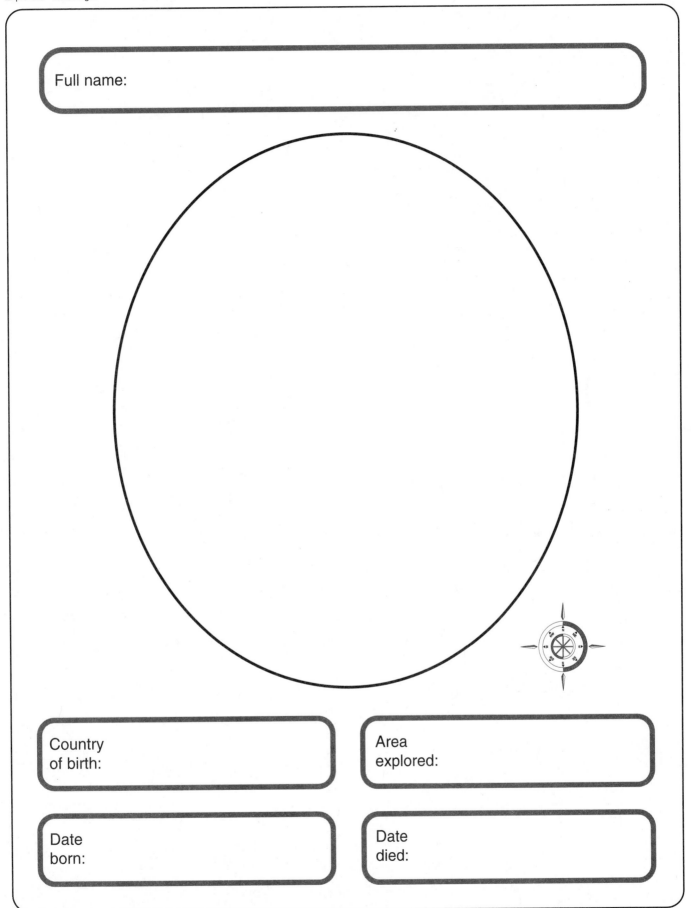

Full name:

Country
of birth:

Area
explored:

Date
born:

Date
died:

More Than a Report EMC 558

Student Directions: Explorers - *An Exciting Report*

Name:____

The explorer I am reporting on: ____

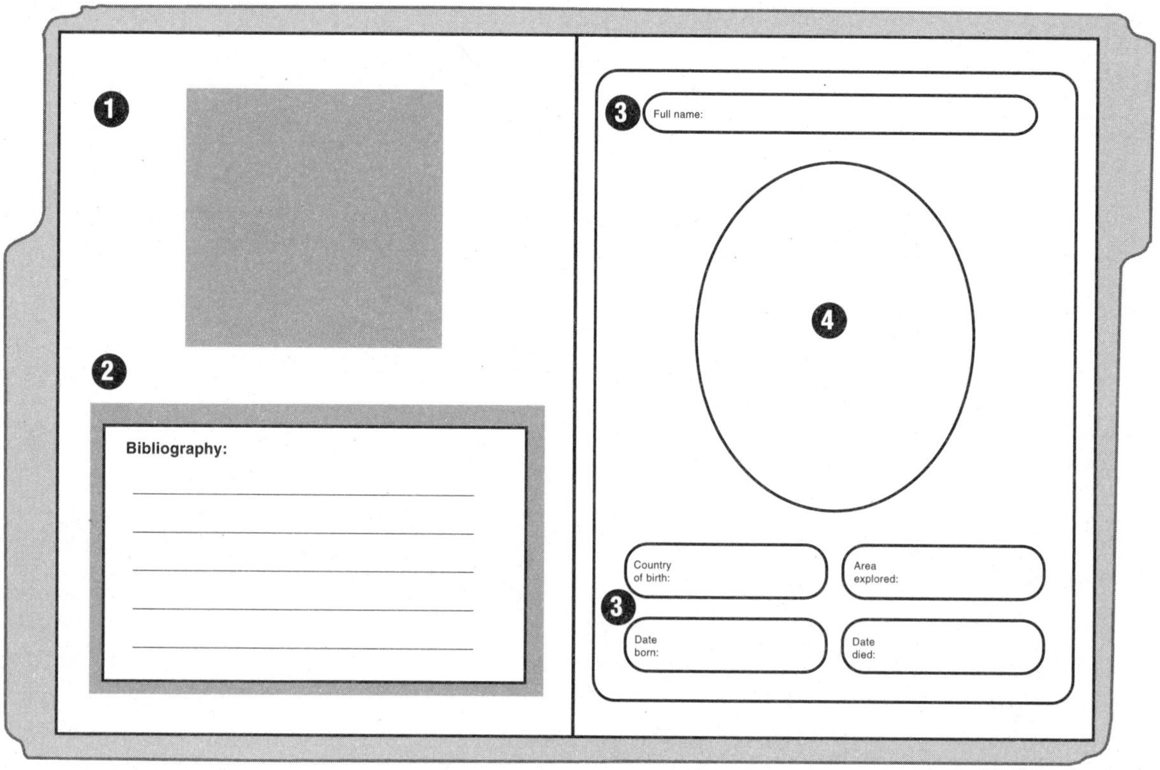

Instructions—The diagram above shows the different parts of your report. Each number of the directions below matches the number above. This is to show you where information is to be placed on your report. Keep these sheets in your folder so you can look at them often. You're going to do an ***exciting*** job and be really proud of your report when it is finished!

☐ **Front Cover**

Your front cover is not pictured here. To complete the front cover, follow these directions:

- Fill in the line with the name of your explorer.
- Draw an appropriate picture in the oval. It should have something to do with what your explorer is famous for. Color it.
- Fill in the bottom with your name, room number, and the date.

☐ **❶ Mode of transportation**

- You will receive a milk carton. Using your milk carton, create the style of transportation used by your explorer.
- You may cut the milk carton apart and glue it back together any way you choose.
- Decorate the model with construction paper.
- Did it have a name? If so, write the name somewhere on the model.
- Attach the mode of transportation to the piece of cardboard you are given.

Name:_____

☐ **❷ Mini-Book**
- This space is for a short, six-page mini-book. You will be telling the story as if you are with your explorer on the trip. It will be told in first person, using words like "I" and "me."

- Use at least two different sources for your information. You may use text books, library books, or encyclopedias.

- The books you use should be listed in the Bibliography in box 2 of your report.

- Here is how to begin each page of the narration:

> *page 1 -* **Join me and** _____ (name of explorer) **as we explore** _____ (area explored).
>
> *page 2 -* **Our journey begins...** (Include: when, where, why and who)
>
> *page 3 -* **It is necessary to pack many supplies.** (Include: food, tools, weapons)
>
> *page 4 -* **Many things happened on our journey.** (Include: hardships, discoveries)
>
> *page 5 -* **The world will benefit from our exploration.** (Include: how and why)
>
> *page 6 -* **As the narrator of this trip, I have made these observations.** (Include: things you've learned, things you would do differently)

- You will be given five pieces of paper for note-taking. Label them: *page 2, page 3, page 4, page 5,* and *page 6.* As you read your reference materials, write down information that will help you write each page of your narration. Write your complete narration on a "sloppy copy" and have it proofread before writing your final narration.

- Your final narration will be written on unlined paper. Paper-clip the paper on top of a lined-paper master so that your writing will be neat and straight.

☐ **❸ Basic Information**
Fill in the appropriate information in each box.

☐ **❹ Portrait**
- With pencil, lightly sketch a picture of your explorer.

- Try to pose your explorer as he or she would want to be remembered.

- Dress your explorer appropriately.

- Add an appropriate background.

- When you are happy with the picture, color it.

Hints for completing an "exciting" report:

Plan ahead. Do not write on the report papers until you are sure of what you want to say.
Make sure your information is accurate and complete.
Use lots of color.
Use your imagination and creativity.
Have fun.

YOUR REPORT IS DUE _____

TEACHER DIRECTIONS

Before assigning the report:

1. Your students will need to be able to do simple research and note-taking before attempting this report. If you feel they lack sufficient experience, pick an explorer and do the research and note-taking as a group, with you modeling correct strategies.

2. Prepare materials needed for each student:
   - 1 file folder or folded 12" x 18" (30.5 x 46 cm) construction paper
   - 1 4" x 4" (10 x 10 cm) piece of cardboard
   - report reproducibles, pages 15, 16, and 17
   - student direction sheets, pages 18 and 19 (fill in date due before photocopying)
   - 6 sheets of plain white paper, cut 7" x 4" (18 x 10 cm)
   - 5 index cards or 5 sheets of paper for note taking
   - school milk carton

3. Decide how to assign each explorer (see the directions on page 3, and the list of explorers on page 21).

Assigning the report:

1. Pass out to students:
   - folder and report reproducibles
   - cardboard
   - milk carton
   - student direction sheets
   - index cards or note-taking papers

2. Introduce the topic.
   - Explain that every student will report on a different explorer. Have students follow along on their instruction sheet as you explain each section of the report (see directions, page 3).
   - Students will act as narrators. Their report will be written as if they are there. Give examples of what "first person" means.
   - Encourage students to use individual index cards to take notes for the report.

Working on the report:

- Provide students with a variety of resources.
- Ask your librarian for support, assistance, and classroom reference materials.
- Set aside classroom time to work on the the reports and to complete the mode of transportation.
- Provide lined-paper masters (see directions, page 3).

Finishing the report:

- Help students proofread work before it is transferred to the final copies.
- Staple pages of the mini-book onto section 2 on the left-hand side.
- Glue the report cover to the outside of the folder.
- Glue the reproducibles inside the folder, one on each side.

Explorers

Alexander the Great - King of Macedonia (356-323 B.C.)

Roald Amundsen - first to reach South Pole (1911)

Neil A. Armstrong - first person to walk on the moon (1969)

Ibn Battuta - Arab who traveled as Muslim Pilgrim (1325)

Charles William Beebe - first to descend 3,028 ft. below sea level in a bathysphere (1934)

Daniel Boone - explored Kentucky (1771)

James Bridger - discovered Great Salt Lake (1824)

Robert Burke - made first north/south crossing of Australia (1861)

Richard E. Byrd - explored Antarctica (1925)

William Clark - reached Pacific Northwest (1805)

William F. Cody - "Buffalo Bill," scout (1846-1917)

James (Captain) Cook - explored St. Lawrence River, Pacific Ocean (1750's)

Jacques Cousteau - underwater explorer (1950-present)

Charles Darwin - explored South America (1831)

Amelia Earhart - first woman to fly across the Atlantic Ocean solo (1932)

Yuri Gagarin - first man in space (1961)

Vasco da Gama - discovered sea route to India by way of Cape of Good Hope (1498)

Henri Giffard - first powered flight (1852)

John Glenn - first American to orbit the Earth (1962)

Henry Hudson - explored the Hudson River (1610)

Henry the Navigator - explored West Africa for Portugal (1419)

Matthew Henson - reached North Pole with Peary (1908)

Alexander Von Humboldt - geographer; explored South America (1799)

Amy Johnson - first woman to fly solo from England to Australia (1930)

Mary Kingsley - first woman explorer of Africa (1880's)

Meriwether Lewis - reached Pacific Northwest (1805)

Charles Lindbergh - first solo nonstop transatlantic flight (1927)

David Livingston - great African explorer (1870's)

Ferdinand Magellan - first successful voyage around the world (1519)

Robert Peary - Arctic explorer who reached North Pole (1908)

Marco Polo - Italian discoverer of the road to China (1295?)

Valentina Tereshkova - first woman to orbit the Earth (1963)

Native Americans

The 33 North American Indian tribes found in the annotated list at the end of this section represent only some of the Native Americans who were living in the United States, Canada, and Mexico when European explorers and settlers first came to the New World. The tribes listed are among the best-known so that students will be able to find information.

To complete this **More Than a Report**, students will research one particular group. The report does not include all aspects of Native American life, rather it is intended to be an introduction.

It is important to teach respect and regard for these peoples who inhabited this land many thousands of years before European settlers arrived. Through the research and completion of each report, students will discover a world of fascinating people and come to appreciate their uniqueness.

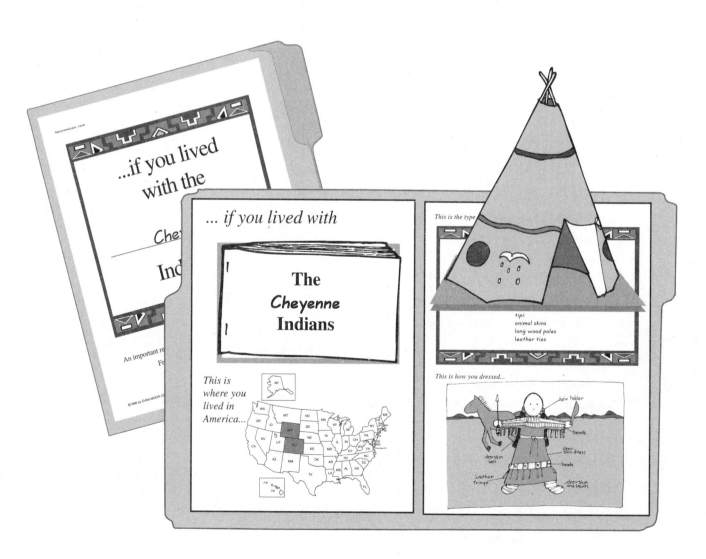

Complete teacher directions for "Native Americans" are on page 27.

...if you lived with the

_____

Indians...

An important report by : _____

From room: _____

Date: _____

... *if you lived with*

Bibliography

_____

_____

_____

_____

_____

This is where you lived in America...

This is the type of dwelling you lived in...

This is how you dressed...

 More Than a Report EMC 558

The

_____

Indians

This is the title page of your report. Fill in the name of your Native American tribe. Decorate the front, color, and cut it out. It will be the top page.

Table of Contents

page

_____ 1

_____ 2

_____ 3

_____ 4

_____ 5

_____ 6

_____ 7

_____ 8

_____ 9

_____ 10

Bibliography _____ 11

This is the second page of your report. Write each question that you have answered on a line. Remember to number your pages and put them in the right order so your teacher can staple them to your report.

Before assigning the report:

1. Your students will need to be able to do simple research and note-taking before attempting this report. If you feel they lack sufficient experience, pick an Native American tribe, do the research, note-taking, and question formulating as a group, with you modeling correct strategies.

2. Prepare materials needed for each student:
   - file folder or folded 12" x 18" (30.5 x 46 cm) construction paper
   - 4" x 7" (10 x 18 cm) piece of cardboard
   - report reproducibles, pages 23, 24, 25, and 26
   - student direction sheets, pages 28 and 29 (fill in date due before photocopying)
   - 10 sheets of plain white paper, cut 4" x 7"(10 x 18 cm)
   - 10 index cards or 10 sheets of paper for note-taking

3. Decide how to assign each Native American tribe (see directions, page 3, and the list of tribes on pages 30 and 31).

Assigning the report:

1. Pass out to students:
   - folder and report reproducibles
   - cardboard
   - student direction sheets

2. Introduce the report:
   Explain that every student will report on a different Native American tribe. Have students follow along on their instruction sheet as you explain each section of the report (see directions, page 3).

Working on the report:

- Provide students with a variety of resources.
- Ask your librarian for support, assistance, and reference materials.
- Set aside classroom time to work on the reports.
- Encourage students to do their research first. As they find information they can use, they should write it down, then write a question to go with the answer.
- Provide lined-paper masters (see directions, page 3).

Finishing the report:

- Help students proofread work before it is transferred to the final copy.
- Staple the pages of the mini-book onto section one on the left-hand side.
- Glue the report cover to the outside of the folder.
- Glue the reproducibles inside the folder, one on each side.

Name:_____

The Native American tribe I am reporting on: _____

❶ *... if you lived with*

Bibliography:
_____
_____
_____
_____
_____

❷ *This is where you lived in America...*

This is the type of dwelling you lived in...

❸

This is how you dressed...

❹

Instructions—The diagram above shows the different parts of your report. Each number in the directions below matches the number above. This is to show you where information is to be placed on your report. Keep these sheets in your folder so you can look at them often. You're going to do a **important** job and be very proud of your report when you are finished.

☐ **Front Cover**
Your front cover is not pictured here. To complete the front cover, follow these directions:

• Using large letters, fill in the name of your tribe on the line.

• Fill in the information at the bottom.

• Color as you wish.

☐ **❶ Mini-Book**
• You will ask and answer ten questions about your tribe.

• Write one question and its answer on each card.

• There are two ways to go about this:

1. As you are doing your reading and find an interesting piece of information, write it on one of your cards. Then write a question that the information answers.

2. Think up your questions first, write one on each note-taking card, and then find the answers.

Name:_____

• You have only ten questions, so they must be good ones. Your answers need to be complete.

• Finishing the mini-book:
   - Proofread.
   - Paper-clip a blank paper on top of a lined sheet so that your writing will be straight.
   - Copy one question and its answer on each piece of blank paper.
   - Add a simple colored illustration to each page if you have room.
   - Complete the title page and table of contents last.
   - Your teacher will staple the pages onto your report.

• All the sources you use should be listed in the bibliography printed in box 1 of your report form.

☐ **②** **Color the Map**
Using a bright color, shade in the area where your tribe originally lived. There were no state lines at that time, but it will help you to understand where they lived if you associate them with the states as we know them.

☐ **③** **Create a Dwelling**
• Construct the type of house in which your tribe lived.

• Make it as authentic as possible; the materials you use should resemble as closely as possible those originally used.

• Stand the dwelling on the cardboard and label the cardboard with the name of the type of dwelling (i.e.: tipi, longhouse). List the materials the actual dwelling was constructed from.

☐ **④** **Dress the Person**
• The figure can be either male or female.

• Use what you learned in your research to draw clothing on the figure.

• Add lines out to the side describing particular aspects of the dress.

• Add hair and anything they would wear on their head.

• Add tools, weapons, or religious symbols in their hands.

• Next to the figure draw one of their means of transportation .

• Draw in the background to show the area they lived (example: plains, woodlands, etc.).

• Color everything.

Hints for completing an "important" report:

Be neat. Use your best handwriting.
When drawing, sketch lightly and erase any unwanted lines completely.
Use lots of color whenever possible.
Use your imagination and creativity.

YOUR REPORT IS DUE:_____

Native Americans

Name	Area	Dwelling
Acoma	Southwest	Multifamily adobe houses
Arapaho	Plains	Tipis
Blackfoot	Plains	Tipis
Cayuga	Northeast	Longhouses
Cherokee	Southeast	Mat-covered houses
Cheyenne	Plains	Tipis
Chickasaw	Southeast	Earth lodges
Chippewa	Northeast	Bark/mat-covered wigwams
Choctaw	Southeast	Thatched houses
Comanche	Plains	Tipis
Creek	Southeast	Thatched houses
Crow	Plains	Tipis
Delaware	Northeast	Barrel-shaped longhouses
Hopi	Southwest	Multifamily adobe houses
Kickapoo	Northeast	Longhouses/brush shelters
Kiowa	Plains	Tipis
Kwakiutl	Northwest	Plank houses
Mandan	Plains	Earth lodges and tipis
Micmac	Northeast	Conical shelters
Mohawk	Northeast	Longhouses
Natchez	Southeast	Rectangular thatched houses
Navajo	Southwest	Domed round houses
Nez Perce	Plateau	A-shaped houses/tipis
Omaha	Plains	Earth lodges/tipis
Oneida	Northeast	Longhouses
Pawnee	Plains	Earth lodges
Quinault	Northwest	Plank houses
Seminole	Southeast	Thatched-roof houses
Seneca	Northeast	Longhouses
Ute	Great Basin	Round houses/tipis
Wampanoag	Northeast	Mat-covered wigwams
Winnebago	Northeast	Bark/mat-covered wigwams
Zuni	Southwest	Multifamily adobe houses

 More Than a Report EMC 558

Clothing Material	Transportation
Skins/Cotton cloth	Horses
Skins	Horses
Skins	Horses
Skins	Bark canoes
Skins	Dugout canoes
Skins	Horses
Skins	Dugout canoes
Skins	Snowshoes and bark canoes
Skins	Dugout canoes
Skins	Horses
Skins	Dugout canoes
Skins	Skin boats and horses
Skins	Dugout canoes
Skins/Cotton cloth	Unknown
Skins	Horses
Skins	Horses
Bark and skins	Dugout canoes
Skins	Horses
Skins	Snowshoes and bark canoes
Skins	Bark canoes
Fiber	Canoes
Cotton and fiber	Horses
Fiber and skins	Snowshoes and dugout canoes
Skins	Skin bullboats
Skins	Bark canoes
Skins	Horses
Fiber and skins	Dugout canoes
Skins and cloth	Dugout canoes
Skins	Snowshoes/bark canoes
Fiber, bark, skins	Unknown
Skins	Dugout canoes
Skins	Snowshoes and bark canoes
Skins/Cotton	Unknown

Women of America

History, as it has been traditionally taught, focusing on political, military, and economic leaders, virtually excludes women. In elementary and secondary school history textbooks women have been outnumbered by men, eleven to one. Studying women of America is a new way of looking at the events and individuals who have made this country what it is today. The study of women's lives and roles can give students a broader understanding and appreciation of American history.

This **More Than a Report** will familiarize students with women whose accomplishments have made a difference in our world. The student's completed report will reflect his or her understanding of the woman as a person and as an historical figure. Through sharing their projects, students will become familiar with many important women. Hopefully it will be a springboard for further research.

Complete teacher directions for "Women of America" are on page 38.

Women of America

A great report about:_____

Prepared by: _____

From room: _____

Date: _____

_____

_____

_____

_____

_____

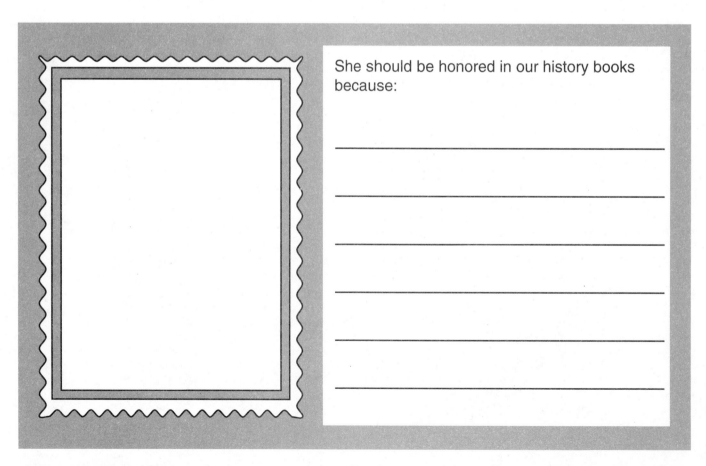

She should be honored in our history books because:

_____

_____

_____

_____

_____

_____

                   More Than a Report EMC 558

Bibliography

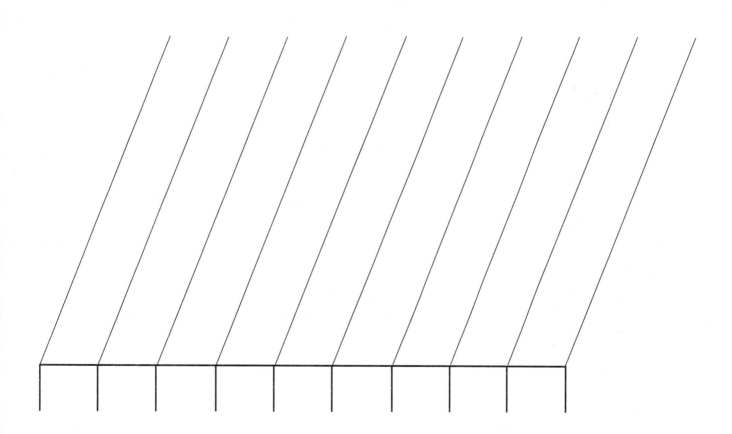

Name:_____

The Woman I am reporting on: _____

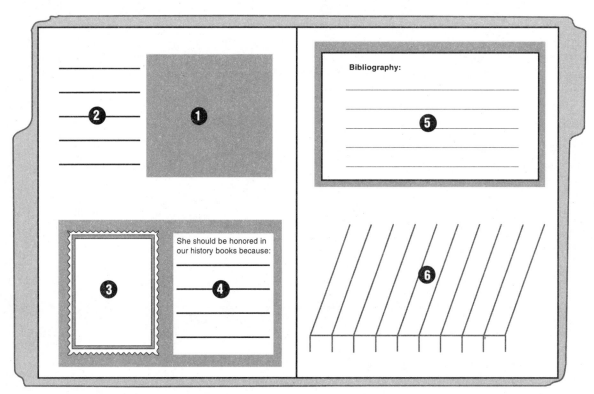

Instructions—The diagram above shows the different parts of your report. Each number of the directions below matches the number above. This is to show you where information is to be placed on your report. Keep these sheets in your folder so you can look at them often. You're going to do a **memorable** job and be very proud of your report when you are finished.

☐ **Front Cover**
Your front cover is not pictured here. Add a portrait of the subject of your report. Then complete the lines at the bottom and color it brightly.

☐ ❶ **Pipe-Cleaner Person**
Your piece of cardboard and two pipe cleaners will be used to make the woman you are reporting on. Your teacher will give directions for making the figure.

• Pose her on the cardboard and attach her with staples or punch holes through the cardboard and tie the feet down with wire or string.

• Dress and pose her so we know why she is famous.

• Clothing can be made out of paper, fabric, etc.

• A face can be drawn on paper and glued to the head circle.

• Use your imagination. You may use anything that you think will be helpful (example: props such as doll furniture, etc.).

Name:_____

☐ **❷ Basic Information**
- *line 1* - full name
- *line 2* - title or occupation (doctor, inventor, singer, etc.)
- *line 3* - complete date of birth
- *line 4* - place of birth
- *line 5* - date of death (if necessary)

☐ **❸ Postage Stamp**
- Create a postage stamp to honor your woman.
- Include words or objects that highlight her life.
- Give it a value.

☐ **❹ Sentence Completion**
Use descriptive words and important information.

☐ **❺ Mini-Book**
This space is for a short, six page mini-book. Use at least two different sources for your information. List the books you use in the bibliography printed in box 5 of your report form.

> *The mini-book should be put together like this:*
> *page 1* - front cover- Be creative. Write the woman's name in large letters and decorate.
> *page 2* - information about her childhood
> *page 3* - information about her education
> *page 4* - information about her private life
> *page 5* - a paragraph about her accomplishments
> *page 6* - information about her later years or what she is doing now.

Using the note-taking cards:
While you are reading about your famous woman, have five cards or pieces of paper ready.
Title the cards: childhood, education, private life, accomplishments, later years or now. When you find information you can use, write it on the appropriate card. Keep all the information about her childhood on one card, all the things you read about her education on one card, etc.

Organize the information the way you think sounds the best. Rewrite it in a paragraph. Proofread for errors. Then you are ready to make your final copy.

Your mini-book will be written on unlined paper. Paper-clip it to a lined sheet.

☐ **❻ Time Line**
- Create a time line of major events in your woman's life.
- The first line drawn represents the year she was born.
- Each line after will be the year of a major event, such as education, marriage, birth of children, and professional milestones.

> ### *Hints for completing a "memorable" report:*
> Be neat. Use your best handwriting.
> Make sure your information is accurate and complete.
> Use lots of color on the cover and around the borders.
> Use your imagination and creativity.
> **YOUR REPORT IS DUE:** _____

Women of America

Before assigning the report:

1. Your students will need to be able to do simple research and note-taking before attempting this report. If you feel they lack sufficient experience, pick a woman explorer and do the research and note-taking as a group, with you modeling correct strategies.

2. Prepare materials needed for each student:
   - file folder or folded 12" x 18" (30.5 x 46 cm) construction paper
   - 4" x 4" (10 x 10 cm) piece of cardboard
   - 2 pipe cleaners
   - report reproducibles, pages 33, 34, and 35
   - student direction sheets, pages 36 and 37 (fill in date due before photocopying)
   - 6 sheets of plain white paper, cut 4" x 7"(10 x 18 cm)
   - 5 index cards or 5 sheets of paper for note-taking

3. Decide how to assign each woman. (See directions on page 3 and the list of women on page 39.)

Assigning the report:

1. Pass out to students:
   - folder and report reproducibles
   - cardboard
   - pipe cleaners
   - student direction sheets
   - index card or note-taking papers

2. Introduce the topic:
   - Explain that each student will report on a different famous American woman. Have students follow along on their instruction sheet as you explain each section of the report (see directions on page 3).
   - Encourage students to use individual index cards to take notes.

3. Guide students step by step to make the pipe cleaner person (see directions on pages 4 and 5).

Working on the report:

- Provide students with a variety of resources.
- Ask your librarian for support, assistance, and reference materials.

Finishing the report:

- Help students proofread work before it is transferred to the final copy.
- Staple the pages of the report onto section 5 of the right inside.
- Glue the report cover to the outside of the folder.
- Glue the reproducibles inside the folder, one on each side.

Women of America

Jane Addams	first American woman to win the Nobel Peace Prize
Marian Anderson	first African American to sing with the Metropolitan Opera
Susan B. Anthony	woman suffragist
Clara Barton	founder of the American Red Cross
Elizabeth Blackwell	first woman doctor of medicine in modern times
Laura Bridgeman	first blind, deaf, and mute person to be taught
Pearl S. Buck	first American woman to win the Nobel Prize for Literature
Mary McLeod Bethune	teacher
Rachel Carson	environmentalist who wrote *The Silent Spring*
Isadora Duncan	dancer
Amelia Earhart	first woman to fly across the Atlantic Ocean
Dolores Huerta	vice-president of the United Farm Workers Union
Emma Lazarus	wrote poem entitled *Statue of Liberty*
Juliette Gordon Low	founded Girl Scouts of America
Susanna Madora	first woman elected mayor of a U.S. city
Margaret Mead	anthropologist
Maria Mitchell	first woman astronomer and discoverer of a comet
Sandra Day O'Connor	first woman justice of the U.S. Supreme Court
Georgia O'Keefe	contemporary American artist
Libby Riddles	first woman to win 1,000 mile Iditarod Trail Sled Dog Race
Sally Ride	first American woman astronaut
Eleanor Roosevelt	most famous First Lady, great humanitarian
Wilma Rudolph	Olympic gold medal runner
Sacajawea	Lewis and Clark's guide through the West
Harriet Beecher Stowe	author of *Uncle Tom's Cabin*
Maria Tallchief	greatest ballerina born in America
Harriet Tubman	former slave who escorted slaves to freedom on the Underground Railroad
Phyllis Wheatley	first female black poet to be published
Jade Snow Wong	artist, pottery maker, writer
Victoria Woodhull	first woman to run for President of U.S.

Black Americans

The study of Black Americans provides a chance for students to reflect on the history of a people long suppressed in the United States. Although Black Americans have contributed much to this country, historically their contributions have not been properly acknowledged.

By completing this **More Than a Report** students will have the opportunity to look into the lives of some of these famous men and women and share the information they acquire with their classmates and your community. Students will be able to observe the qualities of character common to those who have made a difference in the world. Hopefully they may take to heart what they learn and find application in their own lives.

Complete teacher directions for "Black Americans" are on page 46.

Making a Difference

A Report about:_____

Famous for:_____

_____

Prepared by: _____

Date:_____

This famous Black American's contribution was:

_____

_____

_____

_____

_____

_____

Bibliography

_____

_____

_____

_____

_____

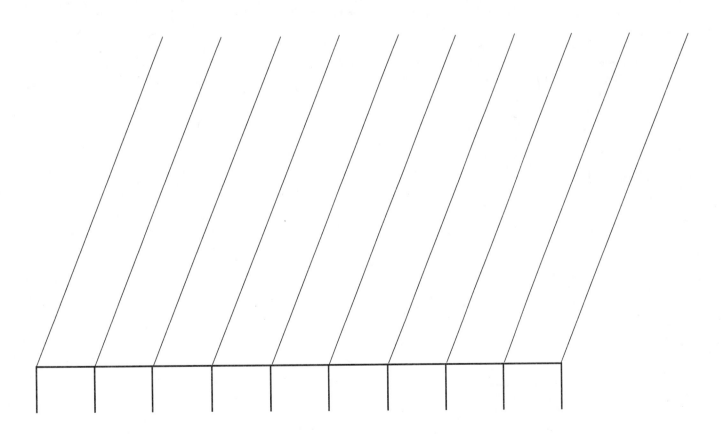

Name:_____

The Black American I am reporting on: _____

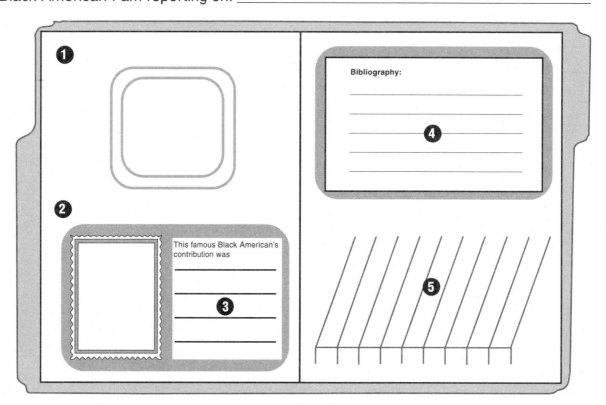

Instructions—The diagram above shows the different parts of your report. Each number of the directions below matches the number above. This is to show you where information is to be placed on your report. Keep these sheets in your folder so you can look at them often. You're going to do an *inspired* job and be very proud of your report when you are finished.

☐ **Front Cover**
Your front cover is not pictured here. Complete the lines. In the box, draw a symbol or something that best represents your famous person.

☐ ❶ **Pipe Cleaner Person**
Your piece of cardboard and two pipe cleaners will be used to make the person you are reporting on. Your teacher will give directions for making the figure.

- • Pose the figure on the cardboard and attach with staples or punch holes through the cardboard.

- • Dress and pose the person so we know why he/she is famous.

- • Clothing can be made out of paper, fabric, etc.

- • A face can be drawn on paper and glued to the head circle.

- • Use your imagination. You may use anything that you think will be helpful.

☐ ❷ **Postage Stamp**
- • Create a postage stamp to honor your person.

- • Include words or objects that highlight his/her life.

- • Give it a value.

- • Color it appropriately.

Name:_____

☐ ❸ **Sentence Completion**
Use descriptive words and include important information.

☐ ❹ **Mini-Book**
This space is for a short, six-page mini-book. Use at least two different sources for your information. The books you use should be listed in the Bibliography printed in box 4 of your report form.

> *The mini-report should be put together like this:*
> *page 1* - front cover- Be creative. Write his/her name in large letters and decorate
> *page 2* - information about your person's childhood and education
> *page 3* - information about any obstacles they had to overcome
> *page 4* - information about their accomplishments
> *page 5* - a paragraph about what this person taught you
> *page 6* - a paragraph about why they should be honored in our history books.

Using the note-taking cards:
While you are reading about your famous person have 5 cards or pieces of paper ready. Title the cards: childhood and education, obstacles, accomplishments, teachings, and why they should be honored. When you find information you can use, write it down on the appropriate card. Keep all the information about their childhood on one card, notes about their accomplishments on one card, etc.

Organize the information on each card and write it in a paragraph. Proofread for errors. Then you are ready to make your final copy.

Your mini-book will be written on unlined paper. Paper-clip it to a lined sheet so your writing is neat and readable.

Accomplishments

Education

Obstacles

☐ ❺ **Time Line**
• Create a time line of major events in your person's life.

• The first line is drawn for you to represent the year the person was born.

• Each line after will be the year of a major event, such as education, marriage, birth of children, professional milestones, etc.

> *Hints for completing an "inspired" report:*
>
> Be neat. Use your best handwriting.
> Make sure your information is accurate and complete.
> Use lots of color on the cover and around the borders.
> Use your imagination and creativity.
>
> **YOUR REPORT IS DUE:** _____

Black Americans

Before assigning the report:

1. Your students will need to be able to do simple research and note-taking before attempting this report. If you feel they lack sufficient experience, pick a Black American from the list on page 47 and do the research and note-taking as a group, with you modeling correct strategies.

2. Prepare materials needed for each student:
   - 1- file folder or folded 12" x 18" (30.5 x 46 cm) construction paper
   - 1- 4" x 4" (10 x 10 cm) piece of cardboard
   - 2 pipe cleaners
   - report reproducibles, pages 41, 42 and 43
   - student direction sheets, pages 44 and 45 (fill in date due before photocopying)
   - 6 sheets of plain white paper, cut 7" x 4" (18 x 10 cm)
   - 5 index cards or 5 sheets of paper for note-taking

3. Decide how to assign each Black American (see directions, page 3, and list of Black Americans on page 47).

Assigning the report:

1. Pass out to students:
   - folder and report reproducibles
   - cardboard
   - pipe cleaners
   - student direction sheets
   - index cards or note taking papers

2. Introduce the topic:
   - Explain that every student will report on a different Black American. Have students follow along on their instruction sheet as you explain each section of the report (see directions, page 3).
   - Encourage students to use individual index cards to take notes for the report.

3. Guide students step by step to make the pipe cleaner person (see directions, pages 4 and 5).

Working on the report:

- Provide students with a variety of resources.
- Ask your librarian for support, assistance, and reference materials.
- Set aside classroom time to work on the reports and to complete the pipe-cleaner person.
- Provide lined-paper masters (see directions, page 3).

Finishing the report:

- Help students proofread work before it is transferred to the final copies.
- Staple pages of the mini-book onto section 4 of the right inside section of the report.
- Glue the report cover to the outside of the folder.
- Glue the reproducibles inside the folder, one on each side.

Black Americans

Henry Aaron	baseball superstar, broke Babe Ruth's HR record
Muhammad Ali	boxing champion (Cassius Clay)
Marian Anderson	opera contralto
Louis "Satchmo" Armstrong	trumpeter
Crispus Attucks	patriot, died in Boston Massacre
Benjamin Banneker	scientist, helped design plans for Washington, D.C.
Gwendolyn Brooks	poet (1950 Pulitzer Prize)
Jim Brown	football player and actor
Ralph Bunche	statesman and diplomat (Nobel Peace Prize)
George W. Carver	botanist and educator in scientific agriculture
Shirley Chisholm	first black woman elected to Congress
Charles Drew	medical researcher, surgeon, organized blood banks
W.E.B. Du Bois	founder of NAACP
Frederick Douglass	abolitionist
Paul Lawrence Dunbar	poet
Duke Ellington	musician
Alex Haley	author, wrote *Roots*
Matthew A. Henson	explorer, first man to reach the North Pole with Robert E. Peary
Jesse Jackson	minister and civil rights leader
Mahalia Jackson	gospel singer
Scott Joplin	musician and composer
Frederick M. Jones	invented refrigerated truck
Martin Luther King, Jr.	clergyman and civil rights leader
Thurgood Marshall	Supreme Court judge
Arthur Mitchell	director of Dance Theater of Harlem
Leontyne Price	opera soprano
Jackie Robinson	baseball player, first black in major leagues
Harriet Tubman	abolitionist, founded the Underground Railroad
Cicely Tyson	actress
James Va DerZee	photographer
Phyllis Wheatley	poet
Stevie Wonder	musician
Andrew Young	U.S. ambassador to U.N.

Incredible People

The people featured in this *More Than a Report* have all accomplished extraordinary feats. Many of these individuals are not known by the students of today. This report gives students an excellent opportunity to discover their contributions to our world.

This is a fun report that the students will enjoy completing. The goal is to provide students with an opportunity for success while learning about people who are truly incredible.

Put these on display for the world to see. Both you and your students will be proud to show off the finished products.

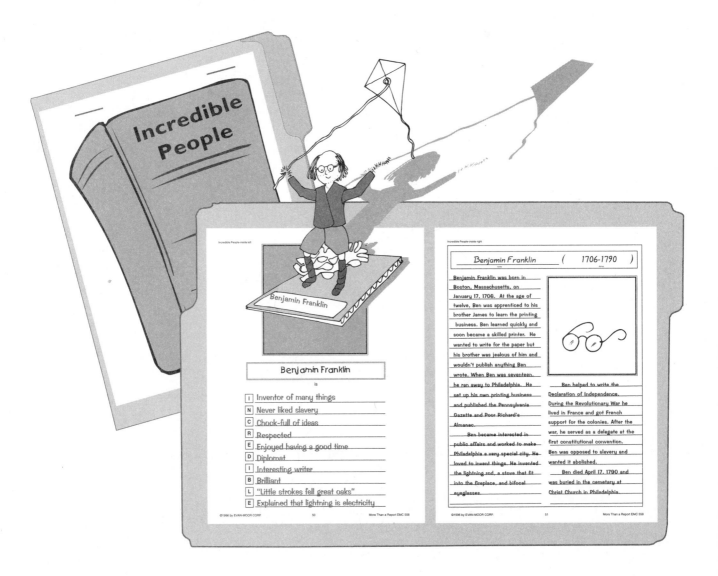

Complete teacher directions for "Incredible People" are on page 54.

Incredible People

Prepared by

From Room

On

Incredible People-inside left

is

I	
N	
C	
R	
E	
D	
I	
B	
L	
E	

_____ (   )
name   dates

Name:_____

The Incredible Person I am reporting on: _____

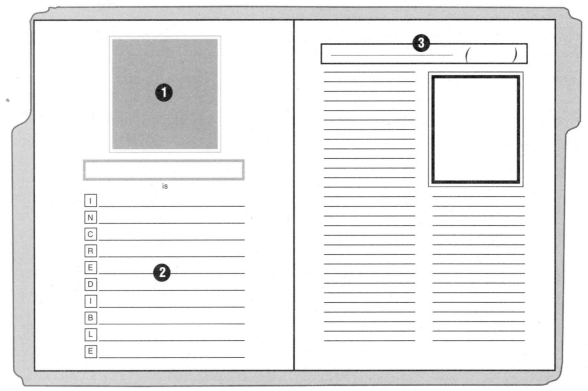

Instructions— The diagram above shows the different parts of your report. Each number of the directions below matches the number above. This is to show you where information is to be placed on your report. Keep these sheets in your folder so you can look at them often. You're going to do an ***outstanding*** job!

☐ **Front Cover**

Your front cover is not pictured here. Write the name of your ***incredible*** person on the line. Complete the lines at the bottom and decorate.

☐ ❶ **Pipe-Cleaner Person**

Your piece of cardboard and two pipe cleaners will be used to make the person you are reporting on. Your teacher will give directions for making the figure.

• Pose the figure on the cardboard and attach with staples or punch holes through the cardboard and tie the feet down with wire or string.

• Dress and pose the person so we know why he/she is famous.

• Clothing can be made out of paper, fabric, etc.

• A face can be drawn on paper and glued to the head circle.

• Use your imagination. You may use anything that you think will be helpful (example: props such as doll furniture, etc.).

• In the box below the pipe cleaner person, write the person's name.

Name:_____

☐ **❷ I-N-C-R-E-D-I-B-L-E Writing**

• To complete the *i-n-c-r-e-d-i-b-l-e* lines you must have first completed your reading about the person.

• The first letter of the line is given to you. The rest of the line can be either individual words that begin with that letter, or it may be a sentence that begins with that letter.

Example:

   ☐ I   inquisitive, inventive, incredible

            or

   ☐ N   Never gave up even though it was tough work

• Write everything on a sloppy copy and proofread before writing on the actual report form.

☐ **❸ Encyclopedia Entry**
In this space you are going to write an article about your ***incredible*** person like those published in an encyclopedia. It should:

   • be written in your own words

   • fit into the space given to you

   • cover his/her life and accomplishments briefly

Read a number of different short encyclopedia articles first to see how they are arranged and what information they contain.

   • Complete your reading and note-taking.

   • Write your sloppy copy and proofread. Decide if you need to cut anything in order to fit the available space.

   • Transfer to the report form.

   • Add an illustration in the box.

> ***Hints for completing a truly "outstanding" report:***
>
>   Be neat. Use your best handwriting.
>   Make sure your article will fit in the space provided.
>   Make sure your information is accurate and complete.
>   Use your imagination and creativity.
>
> **YOUR REPORT IS DUE:** _____

Before assigning the report:

1. Your students will need to be able to do simple research and note-taking before attempting this report. If you feel they lack sufficient experience, pick an Incredible Person from the list on page 55 and do the research and note-taking as a group, with you modeling correct strategies.

2. Prepare materials needed for each student:
    *   1- file folder or folded 12" x 18" (30.5 x 46 cm) construction paper
    *   1- 4" x 4" (10 x 10 cm) piece of cardboard
    *   2 pipe cleaners
    *   report reproducibles, pages 49, 50 and 51
    *   student direction sheets, pages 52 and 53 (fill in date due before photocopying)
    *   index cards or sheets of paper for note-taking

3. Decide how to assign each Incredible Person (see directions, page 3, and list of Incredible People on page 55).

Assigning the report:

1. Pass out to students:
    *   folder and report reproducibles
    *   cardboard
    *   pipe cleaners
    *   student direction sheets
    *   index cards or note-taking papers

2. Introduce the topic:
    *   Explain that every student will report on a different Incredible Person. Have students follow along on their instruction sheet as you explain each section of the report (see directions, page 3).
    *   Encourage students to use individual index cards to take notes for the report.

3. Guide students step by step to make the pipe-cleaner person (see directions, pages 4-5).

Working on the report:

*   Provide students with a variety of resources.
*   Ask your librarian for support, assistance, and reference materials.
*   Set aside classroom time to work on the reports and to complete the pipe-cleaner person.
*   Provide lined-paper masters (see directions, page 3).

Finishing the report:

*   Help students proofread work before it is transferred to the final copies.
*   Glue the report cover to the outside of the folder.
*   Glue the reproducibles inside the folder, one on each side.

Incredible People

Jane Addams	*Hull House—first community center*
Corazon Aquino	*Hope of the Philippines*
John James Audubon	*Painter of birds*
Susan B. Anthony	*Crusader for women's rights*
Robert Baden-Powell	*World Scout*
Mikhail Baryshnikov	*Ballet superstar*
Louis Braille	*Books for the Blind*
Paul "Bear" Bryant	*Winningest coach in history*
Cesar Chavez	*Viva La Huelga!*
Winston Churchill	*Statesman of the Hour*
Eugenie Clark	*Shark Lady*
Mary Decker	*Fast on her Feet*
Walt Disney	*Creator of Mickey Mouse*
Thomas Alva Edison	*Wizard of Menlo Park*
Albert Einstein	*Artist of Science*
Benjamin Franklin	*Master of Many Trades*
Indira Gandhi	*Star of India*
Johannes Gutenberg	*Father of Printing*
Janet Guthrie	*Daredevil racer*
Joseph Rudyard Kipling	*Storyteller*
Ray Kroc	*Mr. Big Mac*
Dorothea Lange	*Photographer of the human condition*
Aldo Leopold	*Father of the National Wilderness System*
Margaret Mead	*Mother to Many*
Maria Montessori	*Teacher trainer*
Samuel F.B. Morse	*Instant Communication*
Anna Mary Robertson Moses	*Grandma Moses*
John Muir	*Protector of the Wilderness*
Pele´	*Soccer superstar*
Jack Nicklaus	*Golfer of the Century*
Alfred Nobel	*Destruction or Construction?*
Ringling Brothers	*The Greatest Show on Earth*
Albert Schweitzer	*Missionary doctor*
Levi Strauss	*King of Blue Jeans*
Mother Teresa	*Sister to Those in Need*
Frank Lloyd Wright	*Master of Light and Shadow*

National Monuments and Memorials

National Monuments are places of historic, scientific, or scenic interest set aside by the United States government as public property. They include structures such as historic forts and natural features such as canyons.

This **More Than a Report** is designed to familiarize students with the variety of monuments and the history behind them. When they are finished with this report they will have experienced the next best thing to actually being there! Through their research they will also learn about our country's past historically or geologically. The information they acquire can be passed on to other classmates, so everyone learns from each other.

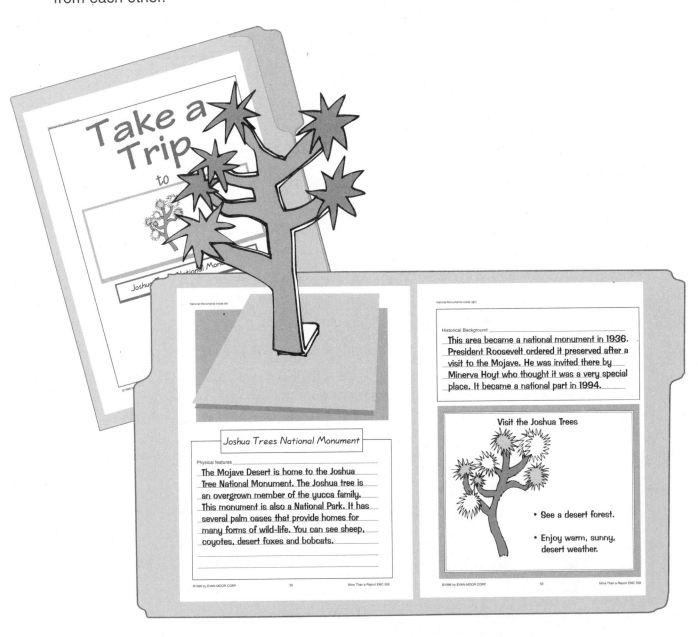

Joshua Trees National Monument

Physical features
The Mojave Desert is home to the Joshua Tree National Monument. The Joshua tree is an overgrown member of the yucca family. This monument is also a National Park. It has several palm oases that provide homes for many forms of wild-life. You can see sheep, coyotes, desert foxes and bobcats.

Historical Background
This area became a national monument in 1936. President Roosevelt ordered it preserved after a visit to the Mojave. He was invited there by Minerva Hoyt who thought it was a very special place. It became a national part in 1994.

Visit the Joshua Trees

• See a desert forest.

• Enjoy warm, sunny, desert weather.

Complete teacher directions for "National Monuments and Memorials" are on page 62.

Take a Trip

to

national monument

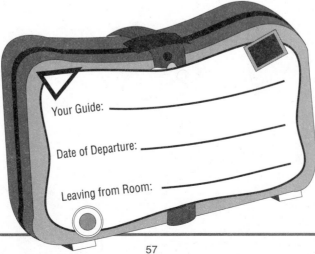

Your Guide: _____

Date of Departure: _____

Leaving from Room: _____

Physical features _____

_____

_____

_____

_____

_____

_____

_____

_____

Historical Background _____

_____

_____

_____

_____

_____

Name:_____

The National Monument I am reporting on: _____

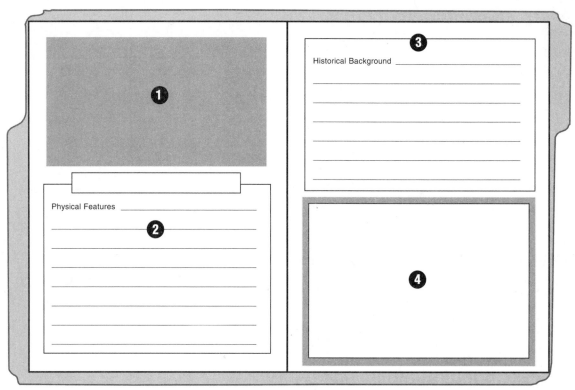

Instructions - The diagram above shows the different parts of your report. Each number of the directions below matches the number above. This is to show you where information is to be placed on your report. Keep these sheets in your folder so you can look at them often. You're going to do a *monumental* job and take us all on a wonderful excursion.

☐ **Front Cover**
Your front cover is not pictured here. To complete the front cover, follow these directions:
• Write the name of your monument or memorial in the small box.

• Fill in the information in the suitcase.

• Draw a picture of the monument or memorial in the larger box.

☐ ❶ **Create a Model**
• Create a model of your monument or a symbol that best represents it.

• Suggestions for materials you can use:

        • Popsicle® sticks   • sugar cubes   • carved soap bar

        • salt dough   • papier-mâché   • foam core

• Mount it on the cardboard your teacher gave you.

• Decorate the cardboard to suggest what surrounds the monument (example: grass, sand, cement, etc.).

Name:_____

☐ **❷ Physical Description**
Write the name of the monument/memorial you are reporting on, in the smaller box in section 2. On the lines in box 2 of your report form, give as many physical descriptions as you can of your monument/memorial. These can include:

- size (height, width, depth, weight)
- what it is constructed of
- when it was built or constructed
- important facts about its construction
- where it is located

☐ **❸ Historical Background**
On the lines in box 3 on your report form, give as much information as you can about your monument/memorial's background. This can include:

- why it was erected or constructed or who first discovered it
- how it became designated as a National Monument
- whether one person was important in this process
- any information you think the reader should know

☐ **❹ Travel Poster**
Design a travel poster to really sell your monument as a travel destination.

- List all the reasons anyone would want to visit this monument.
- Make it as persuasive as possible.
- Draw an appealing picture.
- Use lots of color and detail.

Hints for completing a "monumental" report:

Sketch out your designs on scratch paper before starting your final copy.
Be neat. Use your best handwriting.
Make sure your information is accurate and complete.
Really get to know your topic.
Use lots of color on the cover and around the borders.

YOUR REPORT IS DUE: _____

Before assigning the report:

1. Your students will need to be able to do simple research and note-taking before attempting this report. If you feel they lack sufficient experience, pick a monument from the list on page 63 and do the research and note-taking as a group, with you modeling correct strategies.

2. Prepare materials needed for each student:
   - 1- file folder or folded 12" x 18" (30.5 x 46 cm) construction paper
   - 1- 7" x 4" (18 x 10 cm) piece of cardboard
   - report reproducibles, pages 57, 58 and 59
   - student direction sheets, pages 60 and 61 (fill in date due before photocopying)
   - index cards or sheets of paper for note-taking

3. Think about how students might construct their monuments. You can provide a variety of resources that students may use to construct monuments in class, or they can complete this part of the report at home.

4. Decide how to assign each monument (see directions, page 3, and list of Monuments on page 63).

Assigning the report:

1. Pass out to students:
   - folder and report reproducibles
   - cardboard
   - student direction sheets
   - index cards or note-taking papers

2. Introduce the topic:
   - Explain that every student will report on a different national monument or memorial. Have students follow along on their instruction sheet as you explain each section of the report (see directions, page 3).
   - Encourage students to use individual index cards to take notes for the report.

3. Present potential choices for construction materials and demonstrate construction techniques.

Working on the report:

- Provide students with a variety of resources.
- Ask your librarian for support, assistance, and reference materials.
- Set aside classroom time to work on the reports and to complete the monument.
- Provide lined-paper masters (see directions, page 3).

Finishing the report:

- Help students proofread work before it is transferred to the final copies.
- Glue the report cover to the outside of the folder.
- Glue the reproducibles inside the folder, one on each side.

National Monuments

Agate Fossil Beds (NE)	deposits of animal fossils
Arlington House (VA)	home of General Robert E. Lee
Bandelier (NM)	prehistoric Indian pueblo ruins
Cedar Breaks (UT)	huge natural amphitheater
Custer Battlefield (MT)	site of Battle of Little Bighorn, 1876
Death Valley (CA, NV)	lowest spot in western hemisphere
Devil's Postpile (CA)	lava flow remains in 60-ft. columns
Effigy Mounds (IA)	Indian mounds in shapes of bears/birds
Ford's Theatre (D.C.)	site of Lincoln's assassination
Fort Clatsop (OR)	winter campsite of Lewis & Clark
Fort Sumter (SC)	beginning of Civil War
Gettysburg (PA)	Civil War battle that stopped Confederates
Golden Spike (CO)	Completion of first coast-to-coast railroad
Great Sand Dunes (CO)	largest, highest dunes in U.S.
Homestead (NE)	first land claim under Homestead Act
Jefferson Memorial (D.C.)	circular marble building with statue
Johnstown Flood (PA)	memorial to 3,000 killed in flood
Joshua Trees (CA)	Joshua trees
Lincoln Memorial (D.C.)	marble building with statue
Mount Rushmore (SD)	carved heads of four presidents
Natural Bridges (UT)	three gigantic natural bridges of sandstone
Pipestone (MN)	quarry Indians used stone for peace pipes
Rainbow Bridge (UT)	largest known natural bridge
Sequoia National Park (CA)	largest living thing on earth (Sequoia)
Statue of Liberty (NY)	world's largest statue
Tomb of Unknown Soldier (D.C.)	memorial to all soldiers killed in U.S. wars
Tonto (AZ)	Indian cliff dwellings dating to 1300's
U.S.S. Arizona (HI)	floating memorial to the attack on Pearl Harbor
Washington Monument (D.C.)	4-sided pillar (555') honoring George Washington
White Sands (NM)	glistening white dunes of gypsum sand

U.S. States

The United States of America is one of the most diverse countries in the world—rich in natural resources, full of scenic wonders, and populated with a wide diversity of people.

Though its history is short compared with most of the world, it is complex and deserving of careful study. The format of this **More Than a Report** allows each student to take one state and look at its diversity and its historical place in the development of our nation.

By studying the states and learning about our nation's past, students gain understanding of our nation today. This report can be a beginning in helping students become caretakers of our nation's ideals of progress, freedom, and equality.

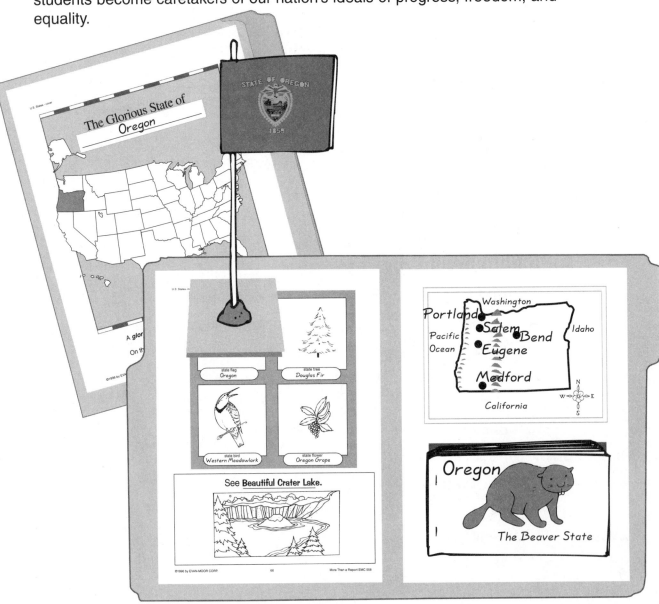

Complete teacher directions for "U.S. States" are on page 70.

The Glorious State of

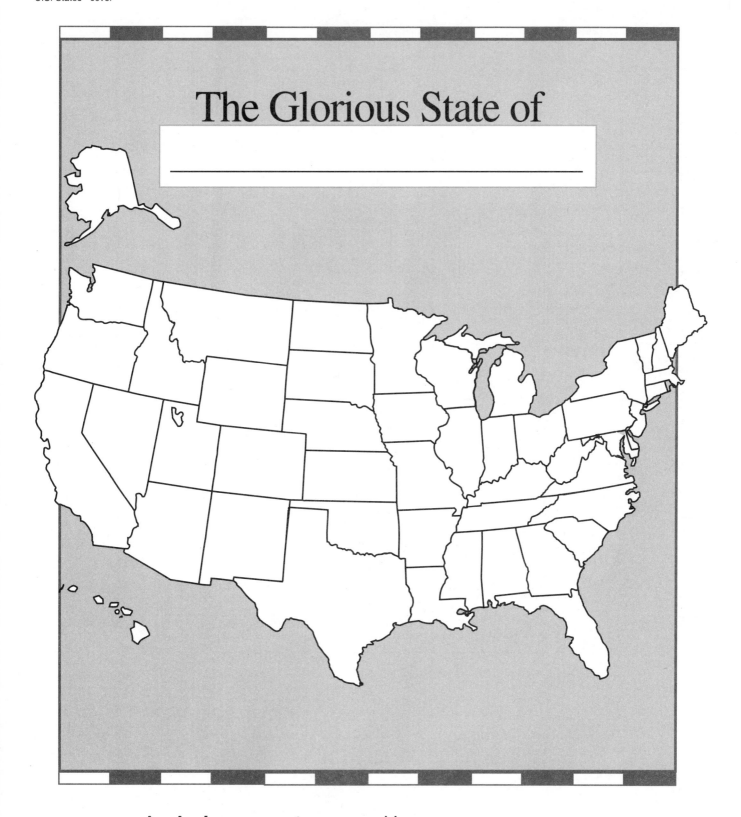

A ***glorious*** report prepared by: _____

On this date in U.S. history: _____

state flag

state tree

state bird

state flower

See _____.

The state of:

N
W E
S

Bibliography

Name:_____

The state I am reporting on: _____

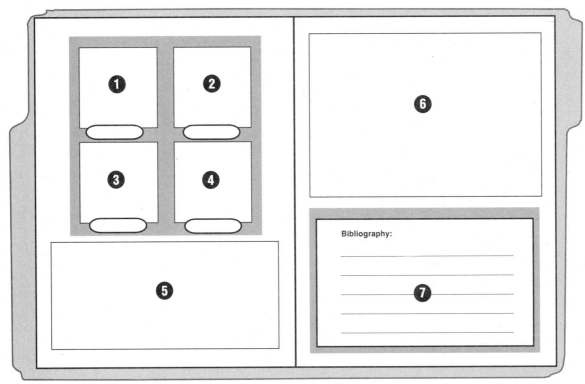

Instructions—The diagram above shows the different parts of your report. Each number of the directions below matches the number above. This is to show you where information is to be placed on your report. Keep these sheets in your folder so you can look at them often. You're going to have fun putting this *glorious* report together!

☐ **Front Cover**
Your front cover is not pictured here. To complete the front cover, follow these directions:
- Complete the blank line with the name of your state. Write neatly.
- Color in your state on the map using a bright color. Do not color any other states.

☐ ❶ **Flag of Your State**
- Fold your 8.5" x 3" (21.5 x 7.5 cm) paper in half the wide way.
- Draw and color your state's flag on one side. Be careful. It is a small and you may need to put in a lot of detail.
- Glue inside of folded paper over flag pole.
- Use modeling clay to attach the flag to the cardboard.

☐ ❷ **State Tree**
- Draw, color, and label your state's official tree.

☐ ❸ **State Bird**
- Draw, color, and label your state's official bird.

❹ State Flower

• Draw, color, and label your state's official flower.

❺ Advertisement

• Advertise a tourist attraction in your state.

• Draw a picture. Use lots of color.

• Add facts that would make someone want to visit that place.

❻ State Map

• Hand draw an outline of your state. Sketch lightly filling up the entire space.

• Label the capital city and the five largest cities.

• Add important physical features.

• On the outside of the map, label everything that surrounds the state (example: other states, bodies of water, other countries).

❼ Mini-Book

This space is for a short, seven-page mini-book. Use at least two different sources for your information. You want to make sure it is complete and accurate. The books you use should be listed in the Bibliography printed in box 7 of your report.

The mini-book should be put together like this:

• *page 1* - front cover - Use all your creativity to make your own cover.

• *pages 2-4* - Describe three events that were important in your state's history. Pick events from three different time periods, so that you give an idea of the state over time. Tell what happened and why it is important. Put one important event on each page.

• *pages 5-7* - Tell about three people from your state who became famous. Tell what they did and why it was important. Put one important person on each page.

You will be given 6 pieces of paper for note-taking. Label them *Page 2, Page 3, Page 4, Page 5, Page 6, and Page 7*. As you read your reference materials, write down information that will help you write each page of the report. Organize the information the way you think sounds the best. Proofread for errors. Make your final copy on the unlined paper. Before you do each page of the final copy, paper-clip the paper on top of a lined-paper master so that your writing will be neat and straight.

Hints for completing a "glorious" report:

Be neat. Use your best handwriting.
Make sure your information is accurate and complete.
Use lots of color on the cover and in the report.
Use your imagination and creativity.
Have fun. Your enthusiasm will add an extra spark to your report!

YOUR REPORT IS DUE: _____

U.S. States

Before assigning the report:

1. Your students will need to be able to do simple research and note-taking before attempting this report. If you feel they lack sufficient experience, pick a state from the list on page 71 and do the research and note-taking as a group, with you modeling correct strategies.

2. Prepare the materials needed for each student:
   - 1- file folder or folded 12" x 18" (30.5 x 46 cm) construction paper
   - 1- 2.5" x 2.5" (6.5 x 6.5 cm) piece of cardboard
   - 1 - 10" (25 cm) bamboo skewer (sharp end cut off) or straw (for flag pole)
   - small piece of modeling clay
   - 1 piece of white paper, cut 8.5" x 3" (21.5 x 7.5 cm) (for flag)
   - report reproducibles, pages 65, 66 and 67
   - student direction sheets, pages 68 and 69 (fill in date due before photocopying)
   - index cards or sheets of paper for note-taking
   - 7 sheets of plain white paper cut 7" x 4" (18 x 10 cm)

3. Decide how to assign each state (see directions, page 3 and list of states on page 71).

Assigning the report:

1. Pass out to students:
   - folder and report reproducibles
   - cardboard
   - "flag pole"
   - paper for the flag
   - student instruction sheets
   - index cards or note-taking papers

2. Introduce the topic.
   Explain that every student will report on a different U.S. state. Have students follow along on their instruction sheet as you explain each section of the report (see directions, page 3).

Working on the report:

- Provide students with a variety of resourcess.

- Ask your librarian for support, assistance, and reference materials.

- Set aside classroom time to work on the reports.

- Provide lined-paper masters (see directions, page 3).

Finishing the report:

- Help students proofread work before it is transferred to the final copies.

- Give each student enough modeling clay to securely support his\her flag on the piece of cardboard.

- Staple pages of the mini-book onto section 7 on the right-hand inside section.

- Glue the reproducibles inside the folder, one on each side.

- Glue the report cover to the outside of the folder.

United States - States and Capitals

State	Capital	State	Capital
Alabama	Montgomery	Montana	Helena
Alaska	Juneau	Nebraska	Lincoln
Arizona	Phoenix	Nevada	Carson City
Arkansas	Little Rock	New Hampshire	Concord
Colorado	Denver	New Jersey	Trenton
California	Sacramento	New Mexico	Santa Fe
Connecticut	Hartford	New York	Albany
Delaware	Dover	North Carolina	Raleigh
Florida	Tallahassee	North Dakota	Bismarck
Georgia	Atlanta	Ohio	Columbus
Hawaii	Honolulu	Oklahoma	Oklahoma City
Idaho	Boise	Oregon	Salem
Illinois	Springfield	Pennsylvania	Harrisburg
Indiana	Indianapolis	Rhode Island	Providence
Iowa	Des Moines	South Carolina	Columbia
Kansas	Topeka	South Dakota	Pierre
Kentucky	Frankfort	Tennessee	Nashville
Louisiana	Baton Rouge	Texas	Austin
Maine	Augusta	Utah	Salt Lake City
Maryland	Annapolis	Vermont	Montpelier
Massachusetts	Boston	Virginia	Richmond
Michigan	Lansing	Washington	Olympia
Minnesota	St. Paul	West Virginia	Charleston
Mississippi	Jackson	Wisconsin	Madison
Missouri	Jefferson City	Wyoming	Cheyenne

More Than a Report EMC 558

U.S. Presidents

For over 200 years, it's been the most famous job in the world. The office of the United States presidency has been held by 42 different men—each with a unique story of how he landed in the Oval Office. Even though they have all shared the same title, their presidencies are different in many ways. Not only are the problems they have had to deal with different, but technology, inventions, and day-to-day living have changed dramatically.

By completing **More Than a Report** about an individual president, students become very familiar with one President's role in shaping our country. As students share their reports and compare the various men who have held this important position, they will become more aware of human differences and the qualities that go into making a leader.

This report requires students to conduct a mock interview with a president, imagining what the president's responses to their questions might be. It is a lot of fun, and the finished results with gallery portraits will be impressive.

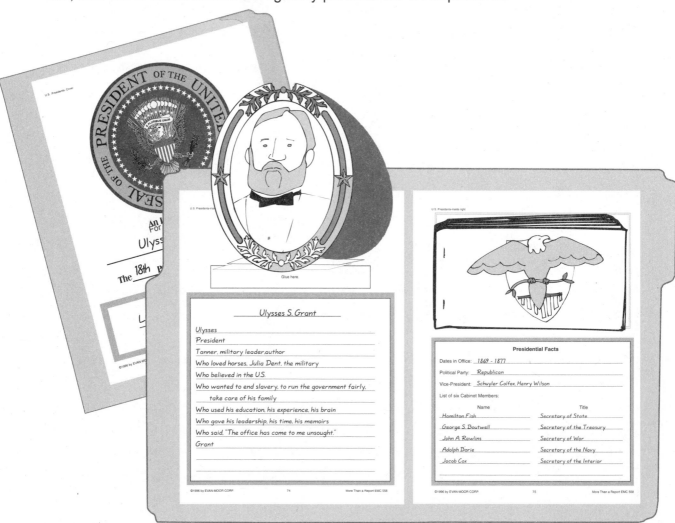

Complete teacher directions for "U.S. Presidents" are on page 79.

An Interview with

_____

The_____President of the United States

Interviewed by

_____

On _____

Glue here.

_____

_____

_____

_____

_____

_____

_____

_____

_____

_____

_____

U.S. Presidents-inside right

Presidential Facts

Dates in Office: _____

Political Party: _____

Vice-President: _____

List of six Cabinet Members:

Name	Title
_____	_____
_____	_____
_____	_____
_____	_____
_____	_____
_____	_____

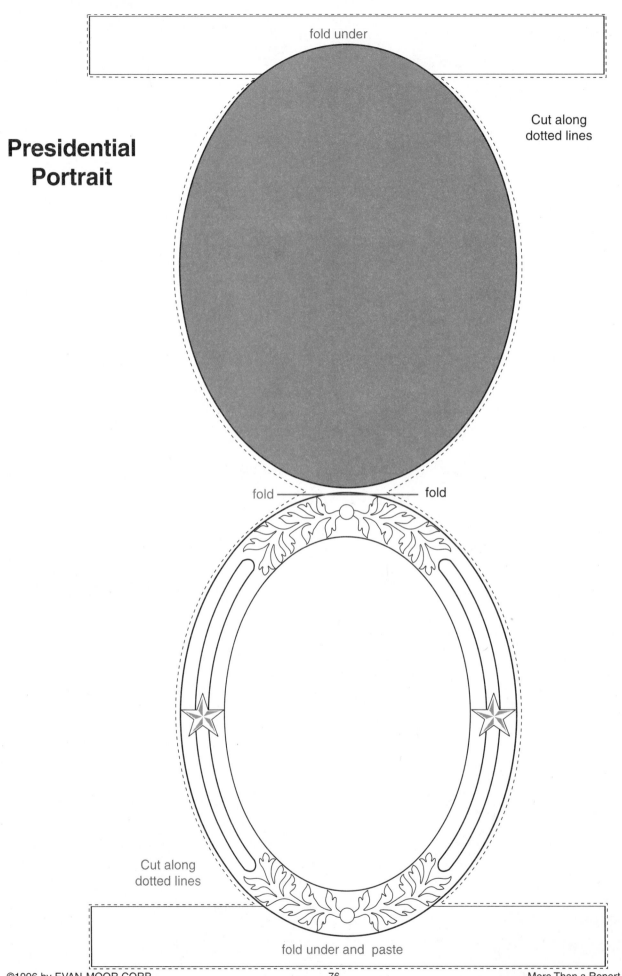

Presidential Portrait

fold under

Cut along dotted lines

fold ——————— fold

Cut along dotted lines

fold under and paste

Name:_____

The President I am reporting on: _____

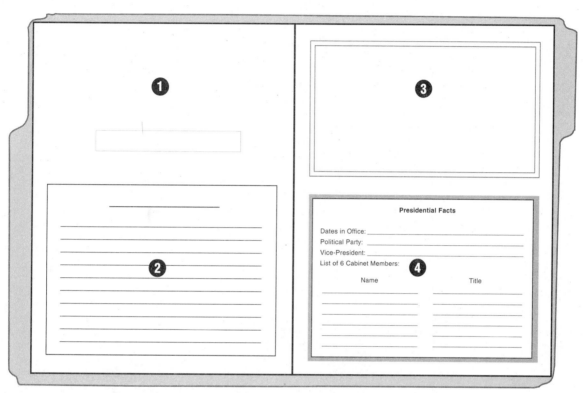

Instructions—The diagram above shows the different parts of your report. Each number of the directions below matches the number above. This is to show you where information is to be placed on your report. Keep these sheets in your folder so you can look at them often. You are going to do an ***impressive*** job!

☐ **Front Cover**

Your front cover is not pictured here. To complete the front cover, follow these directions:

• Complete the first line with your president's full name.

• Complete the second line with the order of his presidency (21st, 34th, etc.).

• Write your name on the third line.

• Write the date on the last line.

☐ **❶ Presidential Portrait**

• Cut and fold the sheet given to you.

• Sketch in your president's head and shoulders only. Do your very best to draw a likeness of your president; do not trace.

• Make it as large as possible.

• When you are happy with it, color the portrait or shade with pencil.

• Decorate the frame with red, white, and blue.

❷ Bio-Poem

Write your poem on a separate sheet of paper. Do not write it on your report form until you are happy with it and it has been proofread.

- *Top line* - President's full name
- *Line 1* - First name
- *Line 2* - President
- *Line 3* - Four words that describe the person
- *Line 4* - Who loved (3 things or ideas)
- *Line 5* - Who believed (1 or more ideas)
- *Line 6* - Who wanted (3 things)
- *Line 7* - Who used (3 methods or things)
- *Line 8* - Who gave (3 things)
- *Line 9* - Who said (a quote)
- *Line 10* - Last name

❸ Presidential Interview

You are a reporter and have been assigned to ask your president six questions. Answer them as you think your president would have. Write each question and its answer on a separate piece of paper. (You may need an extra sheet to answer some questions.) Answer the question in first person (Example: *I was born...*)

1. *Mr. President, tell us where you were born and something about your family and early life.*

2. *Where did you receive your schooling and what did you study?*

3. *Why did you want to become the President of the United States and what were some of the events that led you to such a position of greatness?*

4. *Please give us some background on the First Lady and some of the important things she did.*

5. *Tell us about one world event that happened during your presidency and how the United States was involved, if at all.*

6. *What do you feel was your most important accomplishment as president and why?*

Don't forget to design a beautiful, patriotic cover.

❹ Presidential Facts

Fill in the requested information neatly and accurately.

Hints for completing an "impressive" report:

Be neat. Use your best handwriting.
Be sure your information is accurate and complete.
Use your imagination and creativity.

YOUR REPORT IS DUE: _____

U. S. Presidents

Before assigning the report:

1. Your students will need to be able to do simple research and note-taking before attempting this report. If you feel they lack sufficient experience, pick a president from the list on page 80 and do the research and note-taking as a group, with you modeling correct strategies.

2. Prepare the materials needed for each student:

   • 1- file folder or folded 12" x 18" (30.5 x 46 cm) construction paper
   • report reproducibles, pages 73, 74, 75, and 76
   • student direction sheets, pages 77 and 78 (fill in date due before photocopying)
   • 6 index cards or sheets of paper for note-taking
   • 7 or more sheets of plain white paper cut 7" x 4" (18 x 10 cm)

3. Decide how to assign each president (see directions, page 3 and list of presidents on page 80).

Assigning the report:

1. Pass out to students:

   • folder and report reproducibles
   • student instruction sheets
   • index cards or note-taking papers

2. Introduce the topic. Explain that every student will report on a different United States president. Have students follow along on their instruction sheet as you explain each section of the report (see directions, page 3).

Working on the report:

   • Provide students with a variety of resources.

   • Ask your librarian for support, assistance, and reference materials.

   • Set aside classroom time to work on the reports.

   • Provide lined-paper masters (see directions, page 3).

Finishing the report:

   • Help students proofread work before it is transferred to the final copies.

   • Staple pages of the interview onto section 3 on the right inside of the folder.

   • Glue the report cover to the outside of the folder.

   • Glue the two inside reproducibles into the folder, one on each side.

   • Glue the front edge of the presidential portrait to the report. Do not glue the back edge.
     In this way the portrait can be folded down when the report is closed.

United States Presidents

1.	George Washington	1789-1797	Federalist
2.	John Adams	1797-1801	Federalist
3.	Thomas Jefferson	1801-1809	Democratic-Republican
4.	James Madison	1809-1817	Democratic-Republican
5.	James Monroe	1817-1825	Democratic-Republican
6.	John Quincy Adams	1825-1829	Democratic-Republican
7.	Andrew Jackson	1829-1837	Democrat
8.	Martin Van Buren	1837-1841	Democrat
9.	William H. Harrison	1841	Whig
10.	John Tyler	1841-1845	Whig
11.	James K. Polk	1845-1849	Democrat
12.	Zachary Taylor	1849-1850	Whig
13.	Millard Fillmore	1850-1853	Whig
14.	Franklin Pierce	1853-1857	Democrat
15.	James Buchanan	1857-1861	Democrat
16.	Abraham Lincoln	1861-1865	Republican
17.	Andrew Johnson	1866-1869	Democrat
18.	Ulysses S. Grant	1869-1877	Republican
19.	Rutherford B. Hayes	1877-1881	Republican
20.	James A. Garfield	1881	Republican
21.	Chester A. Arthur	1881-1885	Republican
22.	Grover Cleveland	1885-1889	Democrat
23.	Benjamin Harrison	1889-1893	Republican
24.	Grover Cleveland	1893-1897	Democrat
25.	William McKinley	1897-1901	Republican
26.	Theodore Roosevelt	1901-1909	Republican
27.	William Howard Taft	1909-1913	Republican
28.	Woodrow Wilson	1913-1921	Democrat
29.	Warren G. Harding	1921-1923	Republican
30.	Calvin Coolidge	1923-1929	Republican
31.	Herbert C. Hoover	1929-1933	Republican
32.	Franklin D. Roosevelt	1933-1945	Democrat
33.	Harry S Truman	1945-1953	Democrat
34.	Dwight D. Eisenhower	1953-1961	Republican
35.	John F. Kennedy	1961-1963	Democrat
36.	Lyndon B. Johnson	1963-1969	Democrat
37.	Richard M. Nixon	1969-1974	Republican
38.	Gerald R. Ford	1974-1977	Republican
39.	Jimmy (James Earl) Carter	1977-1981	Democrat
40.	Ronald W. Reagan	1981-1989	Republican
41.	George Bush	1989-1993	Republican
42.	Bill (William Jefferson) Clinton	1993-	Democrat